Grade

3

Name

Matthewson.

Date of exam

Contents

Editor for ABRSM: Richard Jones

Other pieces for this grade

† This arrangement only

First published in 2010 by ABRSM (Publishing) Ltd, a wholly owned subsidiary of ABRSM, 24 Portland Place, London W1B 1LU, United Kingdom

© 2010 by The Associated Board of the Royal Schools of Music

Music origination by Barnes Music Engraving Ltd
Cover by Økvik Design
Printed in England by Headley Brothers Ltd, The Invicta Press, Ashford, Kent

Prelude in C

BWV 939

J. S. Bach

This piece is the first of four little preludes by Bach from a manuscript of about 1727 belonging to Johann Peter Kellner (1705–72). Kellner was a well-known organist and a great admirer of Bach, many of whose organ and harpsichord works he copied out himself. It is possible that the four little preludes were composition exercises supervised or assisted by Bach, rather than original compositions of Bach's own. The Prelude in C is a study in building an entire piece out of a single motive (the first eight notes of the RH part). Mordents might be added to the LH part of bb. 10 and 11 in line with those in b. 9. All dynamics are editorial suggestions only.

Source: Mus. ms. Bach P 804

© 1988 by The Associated Board of the Royal Schools of Music
Adapted from J. S. Bach: *A Little Keyboard Book*, edited by Richard Jones (ABRSM)

AB 3546

B:3
LE RUISSEAU LIMPIDE
(The Limpid Stream)

KOECHLIN, Op.61c No.5

Englischer Tanz in A

No. 19 from *20 englische Tänze*

A:2

Edited by Kurt Herrmann

Carl Ditters von Dittersdorf

Englischer Tanz English Dance

The Austrian composer and violinist Carl Ditters von Dittersdorf (1739–99) was a contemporary of Haydn's. From 1770 to 1795 he was employed as Kapellmeister to the Prince-Bishop of Breslau, who lived at the castle of Johannisberg in what is now the Czech Republic. His huge output includes over 40 concertos, about 120 symphonies and some 45 operas. This English Dance comes from his collection of *20 englische Tänze für das Fortepiano*. Unslurred quavers might be lightly detached. The slurs in bb. 1–5 and 11 are suggestions for exam purposes, but those in bb. 9 and 15–24 are present in the source.

Air cosaque

Leopold Kozeluch

A:3

D.C. al Fine

Air cosaque Cossack Air

Leopold Kozeluch (1747–1818) was a Bohemian composer who in 1778 settled in Vienna, where he was active as a pianist, composer, teacher and music publisher. In 1792 he succeeded Mozart as composer to the imperial court. Many of his compositions feature his own instrument, the piano, notably his 20 or so keyboard concertos and 49 keyboard sonatas. The Cossacks of the title were a people of Southern Imperial Russia, renowned for their military skills. Westerners in the 18th and early 19th centuries viewed them as exotic and bizarre.

All enquiries about this piece, apart from those directly relating to the exams, should be addressed to De Haske Publications BV, Businesspark Friesland-West 15, 8466 SL Heerenveen, The Netherlands.

Sad Song

No. 1 from *Beads*, Op. 123

A. T. Grechaninov

The Russian composer Aleksandr Tikhonovich Grechaninov (1864–1956) studied with Arensky at the Moscow Conservatory and then with Rimsky-Korsakov at the St Petersburg Conservatory. He taught in these two Russian cities until 1925, when he moved to Paris. In 1939 he emigrated to the United States, becoming an American citizen in 1946. His large output includes piano music, songs, operas and five symphonies. This piece is the first in his collection *Beads*, Op. 123, which dates from 1929–30.

Kleiner Walzer

No. 3 from *Jugend-Album*, Op. 25

G. O. Korganov

B:2

Kleiner Walzer Little Waltz; **Jugend-Album** Album for the Young

The Georgian composer Genariĭ Osipovich Korganov (1858–90) first studied in the Georgian capital Tiflis (Tbilisi), then in Leipzig with Carl Reinecke, and finally in St Petersburg, before returning to Tiflis where he taught piano at the Conservatory. He wrote many small piano pieces, mostly for younger players. His *Album for the Young* is a collection of eight short and easy pieces.
Source: Jugend-Album, Op. 25 (Leipzig, D. Rahter, n.d.)

Wilder Reiter

No. 8 from *Album für die Jugend*, Op. 68

Edited by Howard Ferguson

Robert Schumann

Wilder Reiter The Wild Horseman; **Album für die Jugend** Album for the Young

Schumann's *Album für die Jugend*, Op. 68, was composed in less than a month in 1848. At the time, the composer wrote: 'I don't remember ever having been in such good musical form…The pieces simply poured out, one after another.' Some of the 42 pieces were dedicated to his daughter Marie on her seventh birthday.
Sources: part-autograph MS, Robert-Schumann-Haus, Zwickau; second edition, *43* [sic] *Clavierstücke für die Jugend…Op. 68* (Hamburg: Schuberth & Co., 1850)

Tastenritt

No. 7 from *Pianinis*

C:1

Christian Diendorfer

Tastenritt Riding over the Keys

Christian Diendorfer (b. 1957) is an Austrian composer who studied composition and instrumental teaching at the Hochschule für Musik und darstellende Kunst in Vienna. Since 1988 he has been active not only as a composer but as a teacher of piano, music theory and analysis. This piece comes from *Pianinis* (1990), a collection of 22 short character pieces. They aim to be as varied as possible in style and expression but technically straightforward. An acceptable tempo for this piece in the exam would be ♩ = *c.*126.

Stroll On

from *Fun Club Piano*, Grade 2–3

Alan Haughton

Alan Haughton (b. 1950) studied piano at the Royal Academy of Music, London, where he became interested in jazz and associated piano styles. He is a practising classical and jazz musician, teacher and composer. This piece comes from his collection *Fun Club Piano*, which is subtitled *Chill-out pieces to enjoy between exams*. However, there is no reason why it shouldn't be equally enjoyed in a Grade 3 exam!

© 2003 Kevin Mayhew Ltd
Reprinted by permission of Kevin Mayhew Ltd. All enquiries about this piece, apart from those directly relating to the exams, should be addressed to Kevin Mayhew Ltd, Buxhall, Stowmarket, Suffolk IP14 3BW.

AB 3546

Both Sides Now

Joni Mitchell

Arranged by Meredith White